JED PASCOE'S

THE FUNNY SIDE OF

50

FOR HER

First Published in Great Britain by
Powerfresh Limited
3 Gray Street
Northampton
England
NN1 3QQ

Telephone 01604 30996 Country Code 44
Facsimile 01604 21013

THE FUNNY SIDE OF 50 FOR HER
ISBN 1 874125 13 9

Printed in Britain by Avalon Print Ltd., Northampton.

DO YOU REALISE THAT IF WE'D BOUGHT A TELEVISION IN 1963, THIS DAMN BLANKET MAY NEVER HAVE BEEN STARTED

...AND HE FITTED UP THE CURTAIN-RAIL ALL BY HIMSELF!

I'D LOVE TO INVITE YOU IN, BUT WE'VE HAD THE GRANDCHILDREN TO STAY...

IF I WANT TO PROGRAM THE VIDEO...
.. I GET MY THREE-YEAR-OLD GRANDSON TO DO IT!
BIP BIP

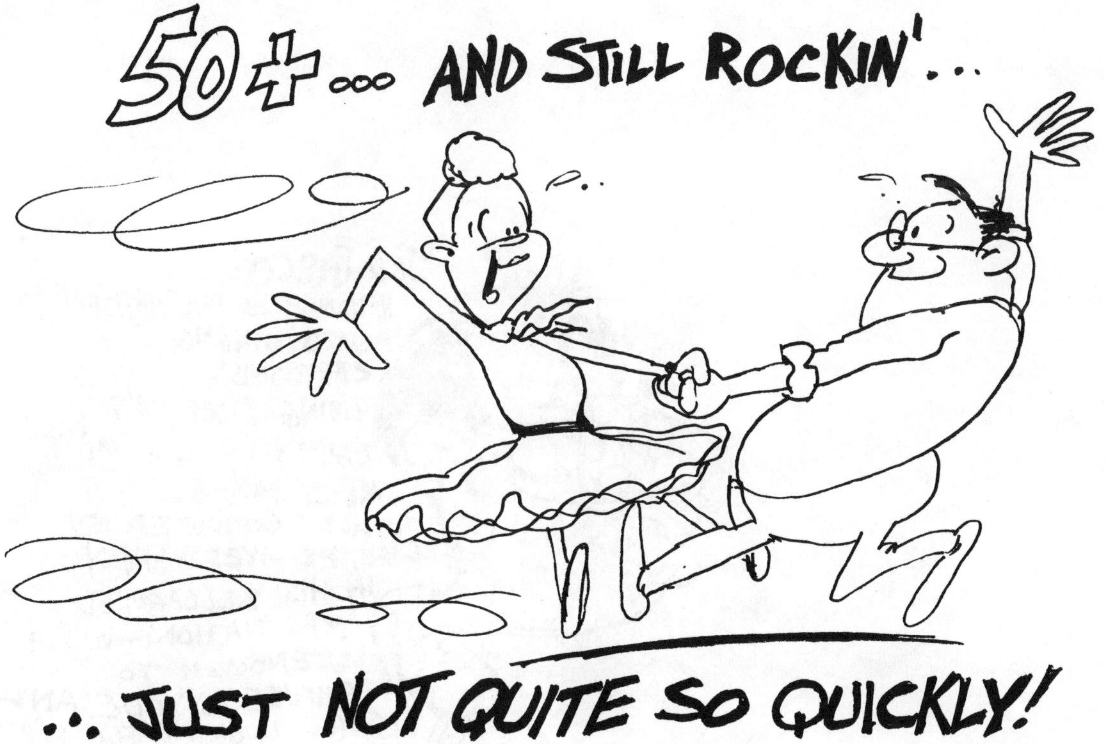
50+... AND STILL ROCKIN'...
...JUST NOT QUITE SO QUICKLY!

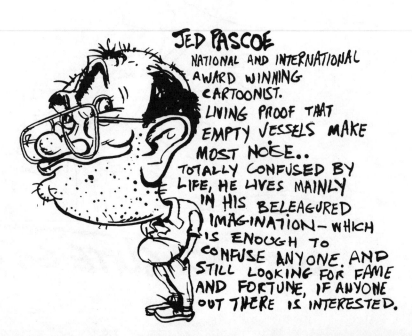

JED PASCOE
NATIONAL AND INTERNATIONAL AWARD WINNING CARTOONIST.
LIVING PROOF THAT EMPTY VESSELS MAKE MOST NOISE..
TOTALLY CONFUSED BY LIFE, HE LIVES MAINLY IN HIS BELEAGURED IMAGINATION — WHICH IS ENOUGH TO CONFUSE ANYONE. AND STILL LOOKING FOR FAME AND FORTUNE, IF ANYONE OUT THERE IS INTERESTED.